Everyone has a Point of View

By
Elyn Joy

Illustrated by
Elena Paun

To Tell The World

Publishing

To Tell The World

Denver, Colorado

Printed in the United States of America
ISBN: 9781726636230

First Edition

The *Thinking Ladder* questions are developmentally-sequenced according to levels of cognition as described in Bloom's Taxonomy of Learning. Original source for Bloom's theory: Bloom, B. S.; Engelhart, M. D.; Furst, E. J.; Hill, W. H.; Krathwohl, D. R. (1956). *Taxonomy of educational objectives: The classification of educational goals.* Handbook I: Cognitive domain. New York: David McKay Company.

For Oliver and Edyth

I see you
You see me, too.

Everyone has
a point of view.

He sees her

She sees you

(And might the trees
be listening too?)

I see sky
while they see cloud

8

You sing softly
She hears loud

He may swim
And she may fly

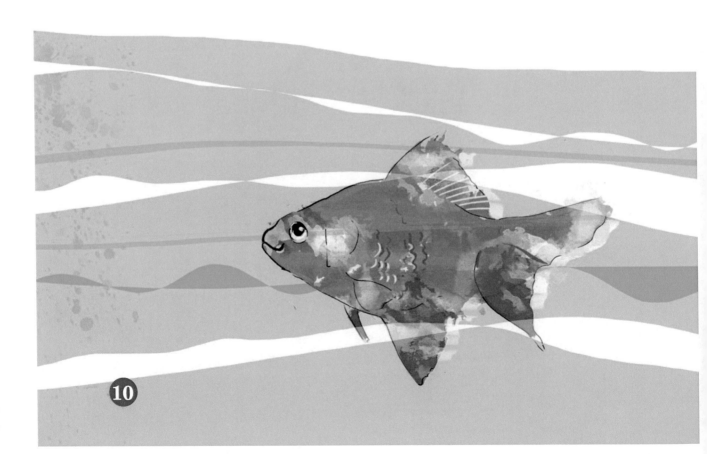

(One rides waves
The other sky)

11

One may crawl beneath the ground

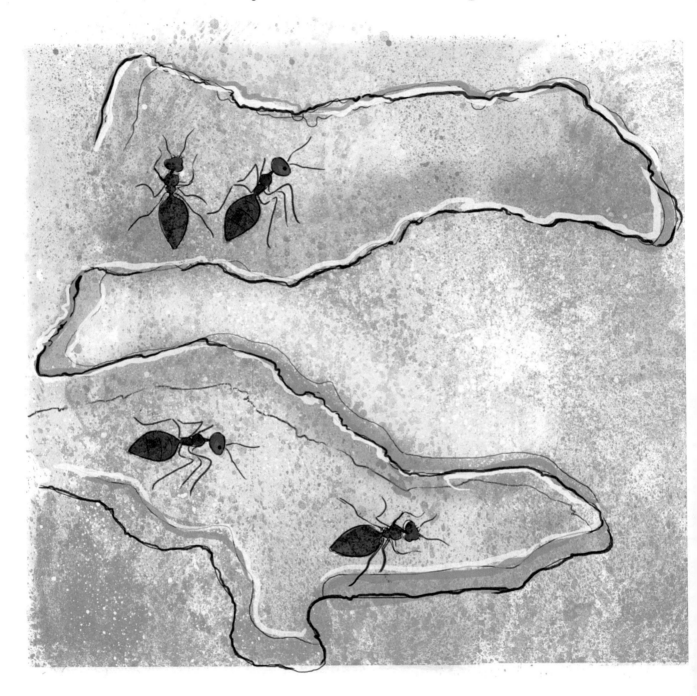

or carry his own house around

But each one has a life so rare

There's none just like it anywhere

15

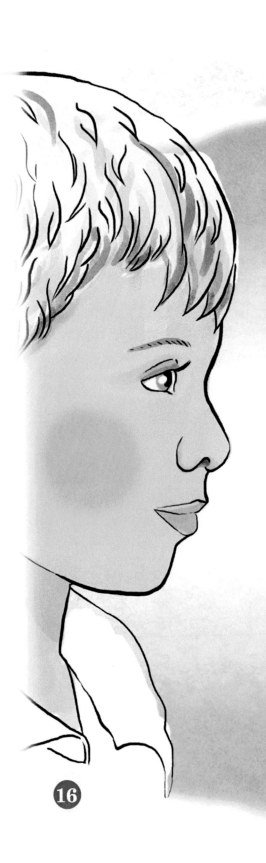

Across the world,

Beyond the blue

One special me
One special you.

Now here is something good to know...

This one's "come" is

That one's "go."

21

This one's "fast" is

That one's "slow."

This one's "here" is
That one's "there"

24

And "here's" and "there's"
are everywhere.

So next time you think
"up" or "down,"

Remember "up" is
down to some.

And if you think it's cold or hot

Another one might say it's not.

Just think of this in all you do:

Everyone has a point of view.

A million billion
passing through

32

A million billion
points of view...

33

...and each one to itself is true.

Thinking Ladder

(Questions sequenced for increasing developmental complexity)

Remembering and Understanding Questions:

1. What does it mean to have a point of view?

2. Name a character who has a point of view in this book. How is his or her point of view different from another character's? How are each of these points of view different from your own?

3. Which point of view did you like the best in this book, and why?

Applying and Analyzing Questions:

1. Can a fish imagine a tree? Can an ant on a hill imagine the ocean?

2. How might a farmer's idea of rain differ from that of a house painter? We all know that rain is good for the earth, but when might it be seen as not so good?

3. What do the above examples show us about the role of **place** in our experience?

4. What does this line from the book mean in regard to place: "Here's and there's are everywhere"?

5. When have you and someone else disagreed on something that was a matter of opinion? Who was right, and who was wrong?

6. Explain this line: "A million billion points of view / and each one to itself is true."

Evaluating Questions:

1. Why is it important to know that everyone has a unique point of view?

2. Is anyone's point of view more important than anyone else's? Why or why not?

3. Is an animal's point of view as "true" as a human's? Why or why not?

4. How can understanding other points of view help us make the world better?

5. *(Advanced)* If everyone has a point of view that is true to them, then how do we decide what is right and what is wrong as a society?

Exercises and Activities for Creating and Expanding:

1. Practice looking at the world through the eyes of someone else: your brother or sister, a parent, a pet, or even a tiny insect on the grass. How do you feel "being" in this other point of view? Practice this often, and follow up with #2.

2. After trying exercise #1 above, draw a picture, write a diary entry, build a model, create a play, or find another way to express the new point of view you tried. This way, you can help others imagine other points of view as well!

3. Practice taking the point of view of something that is neither person nor animal. For instance, you might imagine being a tree with sap in your veins and great patience through the seasons; you could "be" a rock that was once in the ocean but that now rests in the forest. Try to imagine the subject's experience through time. From here, you can either create something new from your experience or research more facts about it.

4. Create a Point of View Collage. Cut out magazines, pictures, drawings, etc., and imagine all the points of view you are collecting! You can write little thought bubbles, or compose a poem, or post single words to help express all the different experiences you've brought together.

Acknowledgments

- *Beatrix Potter, true friend of children and of nature*

- *Ralph Waldo Emerson, lighthouse for the ages*

- *Greg Moldow, steadfast spirit and most loyal supporter*

- *Elena Paun and Deepak Gupta*

- *Dorothy and Samuel Shindler*

- *All my teachers, colleagues, family, and friends who have believed in this project and in me*

*With gratitude and faith in the
wisdom of children,*

Elyn Joy

Love is everywhere....